Table of Contents

Scripture Memory Songs

Learning God's Word Through Music

Credits

Song Compilation: Kim Mitzo Thompson & Karen Mitzo Hilderbrand
Arranged By: Hal Wright
Engraving By: Practical Music Services
Cover Photography: Virginia Dixon

Companion Products

Twin 136CD **Scripture Memory Songs CD** ISBN #1-57583-125-2
Twin 136 **Scripture Memory Songs Cassette** ISBN #1-57583-104-X
(Side 1- Stereo, Side 2- Split Track)

Copyright © 1999 Kim Mitzo Thompson and Karen Mitzo Hilderbrand, Twin Sisters Productions. All rights reserved. No part of this publication may be reproduced, stored in a retrieval system, or transmitted in any form electronic, mechanical, photocopying, recording, or otherwise, without written permission of the copyright owners.

Twin Sisters Productions - 1340 Home Avenue Suite D Akron, OH 44310 (800) 248-TWIN

Give Thanks to the Lord

Give thanks to the Lord, for He is good!
His love endures forever!
Psalm 107:1

Arranged by Hal Wright

14
changes, He stays the same.
A13 A7 D G A
17
He is my refuge, He is my
D G A13 A7 Bm7 E7
20
strength! He is my stronghold,
A7sus D G A13 A7
23
He keeps me safe. So I will lift
D G A D G Em7

26
up His name!
And I will give
A7sus
D G
D
D G Em7
30
my Lord praise!
A7sus
D G
D A7sus
Scripture may be spoken here
33
D
Bm7
Em7 D/F♯ G G♯ø7
A7sus
37
38
Give thanks to the Lord, for He is good. His
B♭7sus
E♭
Cm7

40
love en - dures for - ev - er! Give thanks to the Lord, for
Fm7 E♭/G A♭6 Aø7 B♭7sus B♭7 E♭ B♭7sus E♭
43
He is good. His love en - dures for - ev - er!
Cm7 Fm7 E♭/G A♭6 Aø7 B♭7sus B♭7 E♭
46
He nev - er chang - es, He stays the
E♭ A♭ B♭13 B♭7 E♭ A♭
49
same. He is my ref - uge,
B♭ E♭ A♭ B♭13 B♭7

52
He is my strength! He is my
Cm7 F7 B♭7sus E♭ A♭
55
strong - hold, He keeps me safe.
B♭13 B♭7 E♭ A♭ B♭
58
So I will lift up His name!
E♭ A♭ Fm7 B♭7sus E♭ A♭
61
And I will give my Lord
E♭ E♭ A♭ Fm7 B♭7sus

64
66
praise!
Give thanks to the Lord, for
He is good. His love en - dures for - ev - - - er! - - Give
thanks to the Lord, for He is good. His love en - dures for -
ev - er!
67
70
73
E♭ A♭ E♭ B♭7sus E♭
Cm7 Fm7 E♭/G A♭6 Aø7 B♭7sus B♭7 E♭ B♭7sus
E♭ Cm7 Fm7 E♭/G A♭6 Aø7
B♭7sus B♭7 E♭ E♭ A♭7 E♭ A♭7 E♭

For God So Loved the World

For God so loved the world that He gave His one and only Son, that whoever believes in Him shall not perish but have eternal life.
John 3:16

Arranged by Hal Wright

10
God did not send His Son into the world to condemn the world, but to save the world through Him.
F
C/E
Dm7
G/F
C2/E
12
Dm7
C/E
F
G13
C
F
C
G7sus
Scripture may be spoken here
14
C
Dm9
Em7
Am7
G/B
C
G/B
Am
Fm6/A♭
17
For
C/G
F/G
C/G
G
C
Fm6/A♭
C/G
F/G
C/G
G
C
G
C

19
God so loved the world that He gave His one and on - ly Son, that
C Dm9 Em7 Am7
21
who - ev - er be- lieves in Him shall not per- ish but have e- tern- al life. Shall not
G/B C G/B Am Fm6/A♭ C/G F/G C/G G C Fm6/A♭
23
per- ish but have e- tern- al life. For God did not send His
C/G F/G C/G G C G C F C/E
25
Son in- to the world to con - demn the world, but to save the world through Him.
Dm7 G/F C2/E Dm7 C/E F G13 C F C

No Eye Hath Seen

No eye has seen, no ear has heard, no mind has conceived what
God has prepared for those who love Him.
I Corinthians 2:9

Arranged by Hal Wright

17
1.
2.
those who love the Lord! No eye has
solo
God's love is so
Cm7 F7sus B♭ E♭/B♭ B♭ E♭△7/F B♭ F7sus
21
God's love is so great! His mer-cy so sweet!
great! His mer - cy so sweet! His
B♭ F B♭ B♭/D E♭ F B♭ F B♭
25
A won-der to me! I'll serve my great
plan is a won-der to me! I'll serve my great Lord.
E♭ Cm7 F9sus F Fsus B♭ F

29
Lord. 'Til one day we meet!
'Til one day we meet! And then I will serve Him
B♭ B♭/D E♭ F B♭ F B♭ E♭ Cm7
33
1x sing
2x Scripture spoken
I'll serve Him more! No eye has seen, no ear has
more!
F9sus F E♭△7/F B♭ E♭/B♭ B♭ Gm7
37
heard, no mind has con - ceived what
F7sus F/E♭ B♭/D E♭ F B♭7sus B♭7

41
God has pre-pared for those who love Him, for those who love the Lord!
E♭ Cm7 Dm7 Gm7 Cm7 F7sus B♭ E♭/B♭
45
1.
2.
solo
God's love is so great!
God's love is so great! His
B♭ E♭△7/F B♭ F7sus B♭ F B♭ B♭/D
49
His mer-cy so sweet! A won-der to
mer - cy so sweet! His plan is a won-der to me!
E♭ F B♭ F B♭ E♭ Cm7 F9sus

53
me! I'll serve my great Lord. 'Til
I'll serve my great Lord. 'Til one day we
F Fsus B♭ F B♭ B♭/D E♭ F
57
one day we meet! I'll serve Him more! No eye has
meet! And then I will serve Him more!
B♭ F B♭ E♭ Cm7 F9sus F F△7/G
61
seen, no ear has heard, no
C F/C C Am7 G7sus G/F C/E

65
mind has con - ceived what God has pre - pared for
F G C7sus C7 F Dm7
68
those who love Him, for those who love the Lord!
Em7 Am7 Dm7 G7sus Am7 Am/G
71
for those who love the Lord!
F♯ø7 Dm7 G7sus C G/C F/C G/C
75
C G/C F/C G7sus C

Praise Him!

Let everything that has breath praise the Lord!
Psalm 150:6

Arranged by Hal Wright

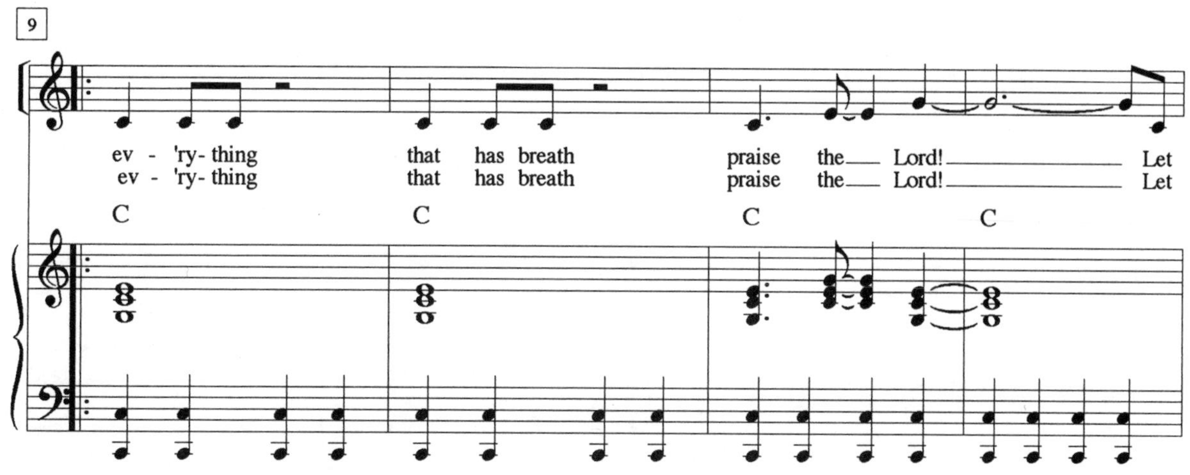

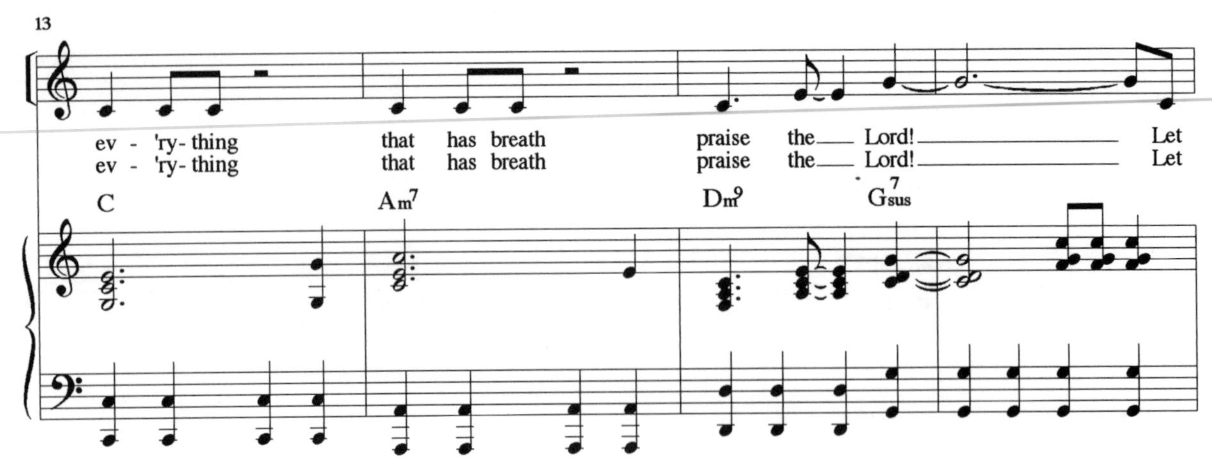
13
ev - 'ry- thing that has breath praise the Lord! Let
ev - 'ry- thing that has breath praise the Lord! Let
C
Am7
Dm9
G7sus

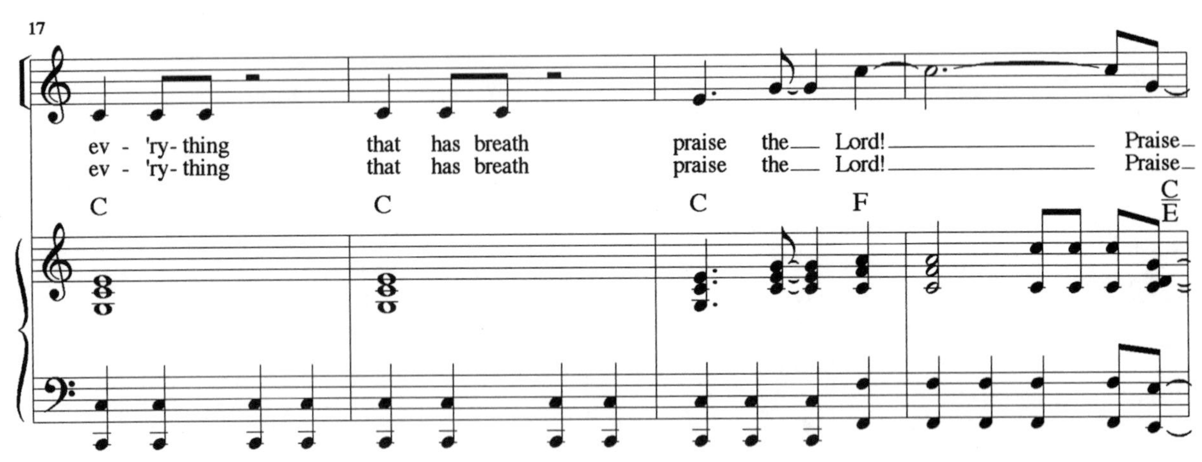
17
ev - 'ry- thing that has breath praise the Lord! Praise
ev - 'ry- thing that has breath praise the Lord! Praise
C
C
C
F
C/E

21
Him with the harp! Praise Him with the harp! Praise
Him with the strings! Praise Him with the strings! Praise
C#o7
Dm7

23
1.
Him with the harp and the lyre.
Him with the strings and the flute.
Let
G^7_{sus}
C
B♭
F
A
G^7_{sus}

26
2.
27
Let
ev - 'ry- thing
ev - 'ry- thing
that has breath
that has breath
B♭
F
A
$A♭^7_{sus}$
D♭
D♭

29
praise the Lord!
praise the Lord!
Let ev - 'ry - thing
Let ev - 'ry - thing
D♭
D♭
D♭

32
that has breath
that has breath
praise the Lord!
praise the Lord!
Let ev - 'ry- thing
Let ev - 'ry- thing
B♭m7
E♭m9
A♭7sus
D♭

36
that has breath
that has breath
praise the Lord!
praise the Lord!
Praise
Praise
D♭
D♭
G♭
D♭/F

39
Him with the sound! Praise Him with the sound! Praise Him with the sound of the trum-
Him with the tamb, Praise Him with the tamb, Praise Him with the tamb - our- ine!
D°7
E♭m7
A♭7sus

42
1.
2.
pet.
Let
Let
D♭
C♭
G♭/B♭
A♭7sus
C♭
G♭/B♭
A7sus
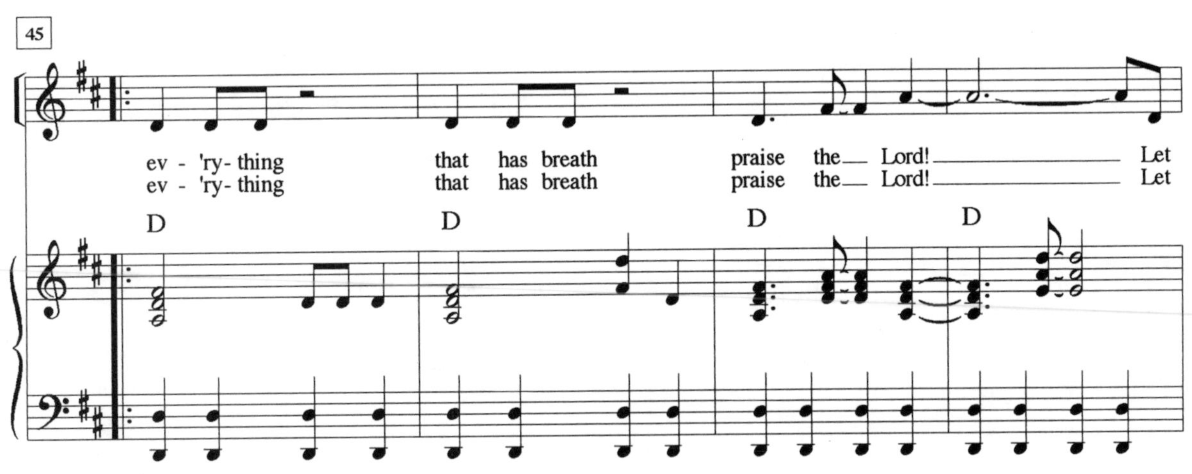
45
ev - 'ry- thing that has breath praise the Lord! Let
ev - 'ry- thing that has breath praise the Lord! Let
D
D
D
D
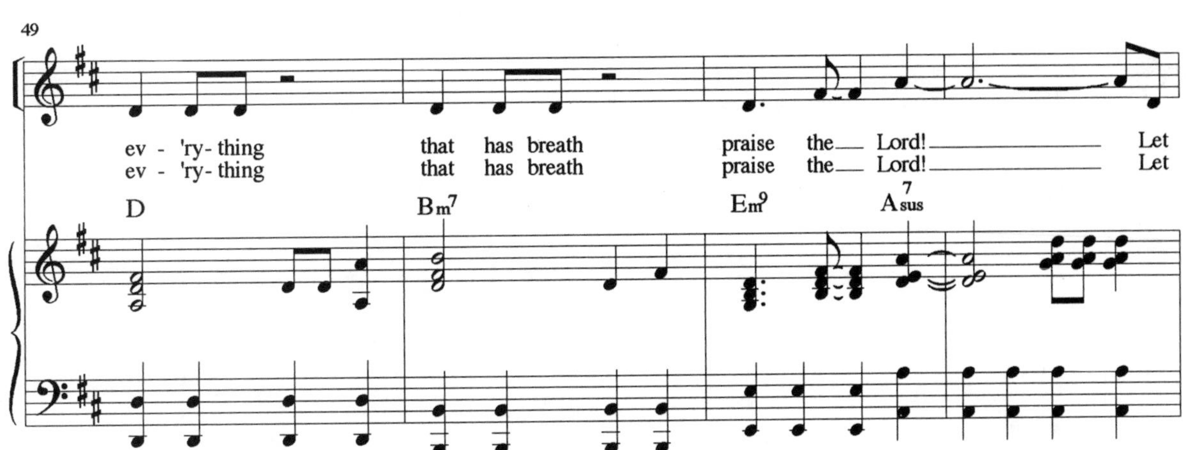
49
ev - 'ry- thing that has breath praise the Lord! Let
ev - 'ry- thing that has breath praise the Lord! Let
D
Bm7
Em9
A7sus

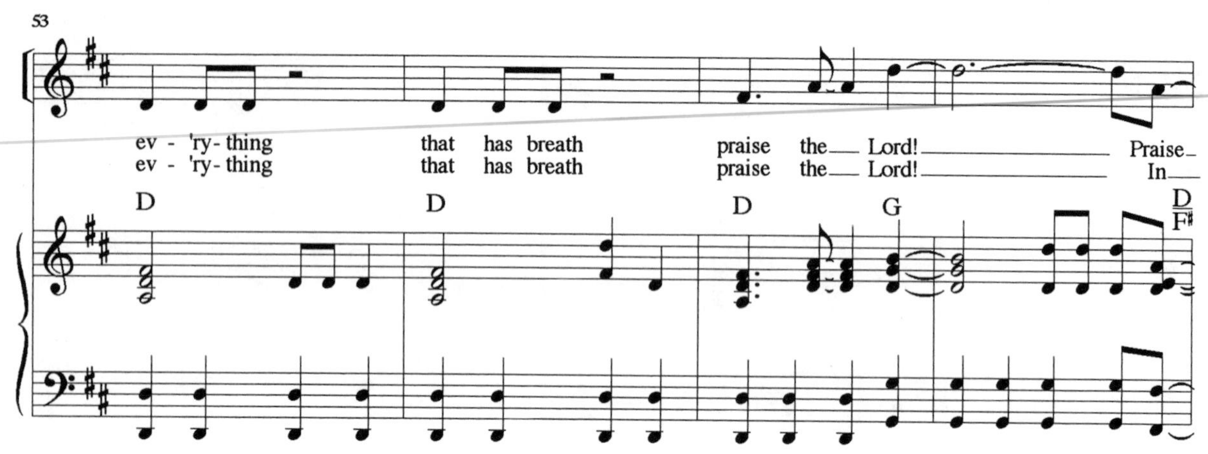
53
ev - 'ry - thing that has breath praise the Lord! Praise
ev - 'ry - thing that has breath praise the Lord! In
D
D
D
G
D
F♯

57
Him with the clash! Praise Him with the clash! Praise Him with the clash of the cym -
His might - y heav'ns, In His might - y heav'ns, Praise Him in His might - y heav -
D♭7
Em7
A7sus

60
1.
2.
bals.
ens!
Let
D
C
G
B
A7sus
C
G
B
A7sus
D
G
D

God Made Everything!

In the beginning God created the heavens and the earth.
Genesis 1:1

Then God said, "Let us make man in our image, in our likeness, and let them rule over the fish of the sea and the birds of the air, over the livestock, over all the earth, and over all the creatures that move along the ground." So God created man in His own image, in the image of God He created him; male and female, He created them.
Genesis 1:26-27

Arranged by Hal Wright

13
God a - bove, He made them all, He made ev - 'ry -
D/F♯ G D/F♯ Em7 D/F♯ G A13 A♭7
16
thing with care and love, God had a plan, for He
Bm Em7 Em7
19
21
e - ven make you and me! God made the earth, He
A G/A A D Asus A13 D Em/D
22
made the sea and He made night and day. God
D Em/D D A7 D

25
made the trees and seed bear - ing plants, and then with - out de -
G/D D G/D D Bm7 G6 G#13
28
lay He made the sun and the moon and He
A13 D G D/F# Em7 D
31
put each star in place. And, ev - 'ry - thing was
Em7 A7sus A7 Bm A G D/F#
34
good that God de - cid - ed to cre - ate!
Em7 D A/C# Bm Em7 A D A7sus

37
Who cre - a - ted the huge Blue Whale that swims through - out the sea?
D D/F♯ Bm7 Em7 A D
40
And, who cre - a - ted the ti - ny fly or the
A7sus D D/F♯ Bm7
43
lit - tle bumb - le - bee? God a - bove, He
A/E E A A/G D/F♯
46
made them all, He made ev - 'ry - thing. With
G D/F♯ Em7 D/F♯ G A13 A♭7 Bm

49
care and love, God had a plan, for He e - ven made you and me!
Em7 Em7 A G/A A D
52
53
God cre - a - ted the birds and the great
Asus A13 D Em/D D Em/D
55
crea - tures of the sea like sharks and whales and
D A7 D G/D D
58
lit - tle fish and birds with squawk - ing beaks. And,
G/D D Bm7 G6 G#13 A13

61
God cre - a - ted the an - i - mals to live up - on the land
D G D/F♯ Em7 D Em7 A7sus
64
like cows and pigs and ti - ny mice and
A7 Bm A G D/F♯ Em7 D A/C♯ Bm
67
tur - tles in the sand.
Em7 A D A7sus D
69
Scripture may be read here
70
D/F♯ Bm7 Em7 A D A7sus

In the be-gin-ing God cre - a-ted the heav - ens and the earth.
And, with each pass-ing day God cre - a - ted

91
ev' - 'ry - thing we'd need. God a - bove, He
A/E E A A/G D/F♯
94
made them all, He made ev - 'ry - thing with
G D/F♯ Em7 D/F♯ G A13 A♭7 Bm
97
care and love, God had a plan, for He e - ven make you and me!
Em7 Em7 A G/A A D
1.
100
e - ven make you and me!
Asus A13 A G/A A D G D
2.

Let the Little Children Come

Jesus said, "Let the little children come to me, and do not hinder them, for the kingdom of heaven belongs to such as these."
Matthew 19:14

Arranged by Hal Wright

13
do not hin - der them, for the king - dom of heav - en be - longs to such as
Gm7 C F E∅7 C♯o7 Dm7 Gm7 Gm9 Gm7
16
17
these. Come lit - tle child - ren,
C7sus C7 C B♭/C C F/C C
19
come to Je - sus. Sit on his
Gm7 C C13 Gm/F F F B♭/F F
22
lap for He has
C/E B♭/D C B♭/C C

25
won - der - ful sto - ries for you to
B♭ C/B♭ Gm7 C B♭/C C F B♭/F
28
hear, a mes - sage of love and peace.
F C/E Dm F/A B♭ Gm7 C F B♭
32
33
F C7sus F E♭
35
Dm7 C7sus C7 F

38
E♭
Dm7
C7sus
C7
41
Let the lit - tle child - ren come, Let the lit - tle child - ren come, Let the lit - tle child - ren come to
F
Fsus
F
F
Dm7
44
me. And do not hin - der them, for the king - dom of heav - en be -
E♭
C7sus
Gm7
C
F
Eø7
C♯o7
Dm7
47
49
longs to such as these. Come lit - tle
Gm7
Gm9
Gm7
C7sus
C7
C
B♭/C
C

50
child - ren, come to Je - sus.
F/C C Gm7 C C13 Gm/F F
53
Sit on his lap for He
F B♭/F F C/E B♭/D C
56
has won - der - ful sto - ries for
B♭/C C B♭ C/B♭ Gm7 C B♭/C C
59
you to hear, a mes - sage of
F B♭/F F C/E Dm F/A B♭ Gm7

62
love and peace.
C F B♭ F C7sus
65
Let the lit - tle child - ren come, Let the lit - tle child - ren come, Let the lit - tle child - ren come to
F Fsus F F Dm7
68
me. And do not hin - der them, for the king - dom of heav - en be -
E♭ C7sus Gm7 C F Eø7 C♯o7 Dm7
71
longs to such as these.
Gm7 Gm9 Gm7 C7sus C7 F E♭ C7sus F

I'm Gonna Learn the Books of the Bible

Arranged by Hal Wright

13
Ez-ra, Job or Ne-hem - i - ah, I'll know where to turn to
F
Gm7
16
Jer - e - mi - ah for I'm learn-ing all the books to-day.
Am7 D+9 Gm7 Csus7 C F Csus7
19
Gen - e - sis, Ex - o - dus, Lev - i - ti - cus, Num - bers, Deu-ter-on-o-my.
F Dm7 Csus7 C F
22
Josh-u-a, Judg - es, Ruth and Sam - uel,
Csus7 F Dm7

25
there are two of these!
First and Sec - ond Kings. First
G7 C7sus F Gm7
28
and Sec - ond Chron - i - cles, Ez - ra, Ne - hem - i - ah, Esth - er, Job,
F/A B♭6 F/C A/C♯ Dm
31
Psalms and Pro - verbs, Ec - cles - i - as - tes, then there's Song of Songs.
F/C F/C C7sus
34
I - sai - ah, Jer - e - mi - ah, Lam -
F

37
en - ta - tions, E - zek - i - el.
Dm7 C7sus C F C7sus
40
Dan - iel, Ho - se - a, Joel and A - mos. O - ba - di - ah.
F Dm7 G7 C7sus
43
Jo - nah and Mi - cah, Na - hum and Ha - bak - kuk,
F Gm7
46
Zeph - a - ni - ah, Hag - ga - i, Zech - a ri - ah, we're al -
F/A B♭6 F/C A/C♯ Dm F/C

49
most through, the last is Mal - a - chi. I have just
F/C
C7sus
52
learned the books of the Bi - ble. I have just learned those books to - day.
B♭
C
F
B♭
C
C7sus
55
I have just learned the books of the Bi - ble. I just can't
F
B♭
C
F
Dm
58
wait 'til Sun - - - day!
Gm7
C7sus
C7
F

Go Into All the World

Go into all the world and preach the good news to all creation!
Mark 16:15

13
preach the good news, preach the good news, the good news to all cre -
B♭ Dm7 E♭
16
a - - - - - tion!
C7sus F E♭ Cm7 F
19
Tell of the wonders of Je - sus. Tell of His in - fin - ite
Tell of the won - ders of Je - sus. Tell how your life is
C/B♭ F/A C F C/B♭ F/A
22
grace. Tell of His love and His mer - cy. Show
new. Tell how He meets all your needs, and tell
C F/E♭ B♭/D A/C♯ Dm

25
27
by your life He's the way.
how His word is so true.
Tell that He came just to
Tell the sweet sto - ries of
Gm7
C7sus
C/B♭
F/A
28
save us. Tell how He died for our sins.
Je - sus Tell how we'll meet our great King.
C
F
C/B♭
F/A
C
31
Tell how God sent us a Sav - ior so a new life we could
Tell how one day with the an - gels in heav - en we'll shout and we'll
F/E♭
B♭/D
A/C♯
Dm
Gm7
34
35
live.
sing.
Go in - to all the world!
C7sus
F
E♭
F
E♭

37
Go in - to all the world! And,
F
E♭
Dm7
39
preach the good news, preach the good news, the
B♭
Dm7
41
good news to all cre - a - - - - - - -
E♭
C7sus
43
tion!
F
E♭
Cm7
F

Rejoice in the Lord Always

Rejoice in the Lord always. I will say it again: Rejoice!
Philippians 4:4

Arranged by Hal Wright

1
C C Am7 F C/E Dm7 C

4
Re - joice in the Lord al - ways! Re -
G/B F/A G C C

7
joice in the Lord al - ways! Re - joice in the Lord al -
C C A Dm7

10
ways! I will say it a - gain, re - joice! Re -
Dm7 Gsus C/G G7sus G C F C G7sus

13
joice! Re-joice! Re - joice! Re-joice! Re - joice in the
C C Am7 Dm11 G7
16
Lord. Re - joice! Re-joice! Re - joice! Re-joice!
C G7sus C C Am7
19
1.
2.
Al - ways re-joice in the Lord. Re Lord. Let your
Dm11 G7sus G7 C F C G7sus C F C G7sus
22
gen - tle-ness be ev - i-dent to all, the Lord is
C G/B Am Fm6/A♭ C/G G

25
near. Do not be an - xious a - bout an - y - thing, but in
C F/C C D/F♯ G
28
ev - 'ry - thing by prayer and pe - ti - tion, with thanks - giv - ing, pre -
Dm A/C♯ Dm7 Dm7
31
sent your re - quests to God. And the peace of God which trans -
C/G G7sus G C B♭
34
cends all un - der - stand - ing, will guard your hearts and your minds in Christ Je -
F/A FΔ7/G C/G G7sus G7

37
39
sus.
Re - joice in the Lord al -
C Am7 G7sus
C
40
ways! Re - joice in the Lord al - ways! Re -
C
C
C A
43
joice in the Lord al - ways! I will say it a-gain, re -
Dm7
Dm7
Gsus C/G G7sus G
46
47
joice! Re - joice! Re-joice! Re - joice! Re-joice! Re -
C F C G7sus
C
C Am7

49
joice in the Lord. Re - joice! Re- joice! Re -
Dm11 G7 C G7sus C
52
1.
joice! Re - joice! Al - ways re - joice in the Lord. Re
C Am7 Dm11 G7sus G7 C F C G7sus
55
2.
Lord. Re - joice!
C F C Am7 G7sus C

On Wings Like Eagles

Do you not know? Have you not heard? The Lord is the everlasting God, the Creator of the ends of the earth. He will not grow tired or weary, and his understanding no one can fathom. He gives strength to the weary and increases the power of the weak. Even youths grow tired and weary, and young men stumble and fall. But those who hope in the Lord will renew their strength. They will soar on wings like eagles, they will run and not grow weary, they will walk and not be faint.

Isaiah 40:28-31

16
17
But those who hope in the Lord will re-new their
G7sus
Dm7
G7sus
G
19
strength. They will soar on wings like
C
Dm
22
eag - les. They will run and not grow wear - y. They will
Dm/C
B♭△7
Am7
25
walk and not be faint. But those who hope in the
G7sus
C
Dm7

28
Lord, But those who hope in the Lord, But those who
Gsus G/F Em7 A7sus A7
31
hope in the Lord will re - new their strength.
Dm7 G7sus G C
34
C C C

The Fruit of the Spirit

But the fruit of the Spirit is love, joy, peace, patience, kindness, goodness, faithfulness, gentleness and self-control.
Galatians 5:22

Arranged by Hal Wright

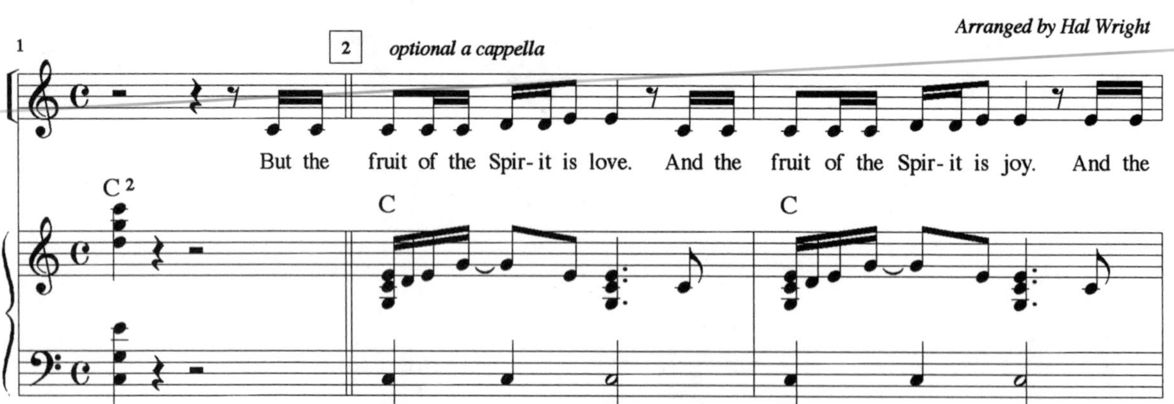

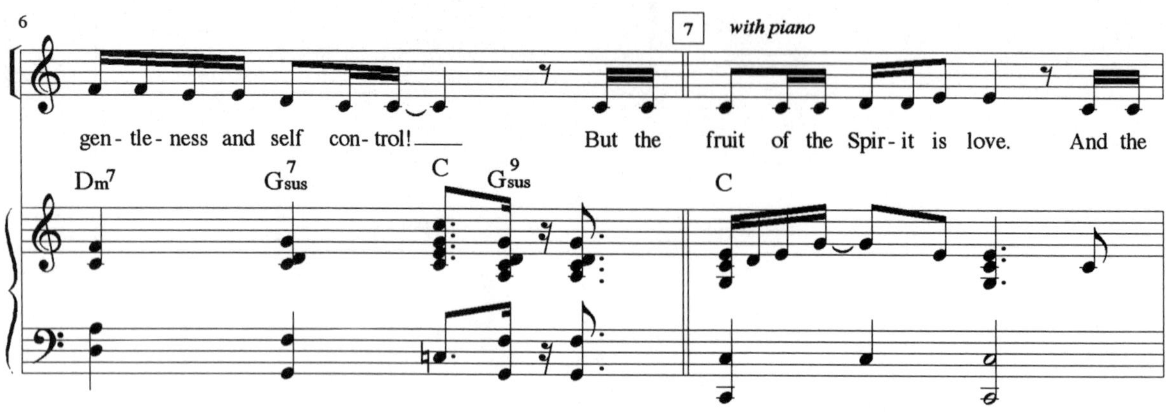

fruit of the Spir-it is joy. And the fruit of the Spir-it is peace and pa-tience,
C
C
kind-ness, good-ness, faith-ful-ness, gen-tle-ness and self con-trol!
C2 Am7 G7 C2 A/C♯ Dm7 G7sus C A♭7
Scripture may be spoken here
D♭
D♭
D♭
D♭2 B♭m7 A♭7 D♭2 B♭/D

16
17
optional a cappella
But the fruit of the Spir-it is love. And the
E♭m7 A♭7sus D♭ A♭7sus A7sus
D
18
fruit of the Spir-it is joy. And the fruit of the Spir-it is peace and pa-tience,
D
D
20
kind-ness, good-ness, faith-ful-ness, gen-tle-ness and self con-trol! But the
D2 Bm7 A7 D2 B/D♯ Em7 A7sus D A7sus
22
with piano
fruit of the Spir-it is love. And the fruit of the Spir-it is joy. And the
D
D

24
fruit of the Spir- it is peace and pa- tience, kind- ness, good- ness, faith - ful- ness,
D D2 Bm7 A7 D2 B/D♯
26
27
gen- tle- ness and self con- trol! But the fruit of the Spir- it is love. And the
Em7 A7sus D B♭7 E♭
28
fruit of the Spir- it is joy. And the fruit of the Spir- it is peace and pa- tience,
E♭ E♭
30
kind- ness, good- ness, faith - ful- ness, gen- tle- ness and self con- trol!
E♭2 Cm7 B♭7 E♭2 C/E Fm7 B♭7sus E♭

Saved by Grace

For it is by grace you have been saved,
through faith and this not from yourselves, it is the gift of God.
Ephesians 2:8

10
act, and what I say, it's not e-nough to save me for I am
me and so I say, e - tern - al life with Je - sus is a
B♭m11
A♭5 9
A♭
E♭/G
Cm
12
saved by grace!
gift that you should take.
I have been
Fm7
B♭7
E♭
E♭
Cm7
B♭sus 7
B♭13
14
saved by grace, God's won - der - ful grace. His
E♭
F/A
B♭
16
spe - cial gift to me for I be - lieve that Je - sus died for me. I have been
E♭
Cm7
Fm7
B♭

18
saved by grace, God's won - der - ful grace. His
E♭ F/A B♭
20
spe - cial gift to me for I be - lieve that Je - sus died for me. I am a
E♭ Cm7 Fm7 B♭
22
sin - ner now made clean, for I've been saved by
E♭ Cm7 Fm7 B♭7sus B♭7
24
1. 2.
grace! It grace!
E♭ B♭sus B♭ E♭ A♭ E♭

The New Testament Song

9
First and Sec - ond Tim - o - thy,
Ti - tus and Phi - le - mon.
D Bm7 Em7 D/F♯ G6 G♯ø7 D/A A7 D
11
He - brews, next is James,
First and Sec - ond Pe - ter.
D/F♯ F Em11 Asus
13
First John, Sec - ond John, Third John,
Jude and Rev - e - la - tion!
D Bm7 Em7 D/F♯ G6 G♯ø7 D/A A7 D
15
16
G F♯m7 Em7 A D A7 D Bm7

17 Em7 D/F♯ G6 G♯ø7 D/A A7 D D Bm7
19 Em7 D/F♯ G6 G♯ø7 D/A A7 D D/F♯ F
21 Em11 Asus D Bm7
23 Em7 D/F♯ G6 G♯ø7 D/A A7 D D/F♯ F
25 Em11 Asus D Bm7
27 Em7 D/F♯ G6 G♯ø7 D/A A7 D G F♯m7 Em7 A D A7

29
Mat - thew, Mark, Luke and John, Acts and next is Ro - mans.
D Bm7 Em7 D/F♯ G6 G♯ø7 D/A A7 D
31
First and Sec - ond Cor - in - thi - ans, Ga - la - tions and E - phe - sians. Phil -
D Bm7 Em7 D/F♯ G6 G♯ø7 D/A A7 D
33
ip - pi - ans, Co - los - sians, First and Sec - ond Thes - sa - lon - i - ans,
D/F♯ F Em11 Asus
35
First and Sec - ond Tim - o - thy, Ti - tus and Phi - le - mon.
D Bm7 Em7 D/F♯ G6 G♯ø7 D/A A7 D

37
He - brews, next is James, First and Sec - ond Pe - ter.
D/F♯ F Em11 Asus
39
First John, Sec - ond John, Third John, Jude and Rev - e - la - tion!
D Bm7 Em7 D/F♯ G6 G♯ø7 D/A A7 D
41
G F♯m7 Em7 A D

Do To Others

Do to others as you would have them do to you.
Luke 6:31

Arranged by Hal Wright

10
do to oth-ers, yes you should, do to oth-ers as you would
B♭ A♭/B♭ B♭13 B♭/A♭ E♭/G C7sus E°7
12
have them do to you! Some -
Fm7 E♭/B♭ B♭ E♭ A♭ E♭ B♭7sus
14
times my bro-ther both-ers me. He tags a-long with my friends and he has
cous-in thinks she's al-ways right and her green hair is out of sight. She
E♭ E♭
16
dir-ty hands and a run-ny nose. But I should be kind I sup-pose. My
brags and tells me she's the best. It's
E♭ B♭/D Cm F7 B♭
1.

18
2.
spoken
hard to love her I con-fess.
But the Bi - ble says,
F7 B♭ B♭ A♭/B♭ B♭7
20
Do to oth - ers as you would have them do to you!
E♭ E♭/G B♭ A♭/C B♭/D
22
Do to oth - ers as you would have them do to you!
E♭ Cm7 B♭ F7 B♭
24
Do to oth-ers, do to oth-ers, do to oth-ers, yes you should,
B♭ A♭/B♭ B♭13 B♭ B♭ A♭/B♭ B♭13 B♭/A♭

26
do to oth-ers as you— would have— them— do to you! My
E♭/G C7sus E°7 Fm7 E♭/B♭ B♭ E♭ A♭ E♭ B♭7sus
29
moth-er says, "It's time for bed." "That's not fair!" goes through my head. But
new stu-dent ar-rived at school. He's kind of shy and not too cool. But
E♭ E♭
31
I know that— my— mom is right and I
I in-vit-ed him to play some hoops. He said,
E♭ B♭/D Cm
1.
lis-ten and say, "Good night!" A
F7 B♭
33
2.
"Thanks!"— as he joined our group.—
F7 B♭
spoken
For the Bi-ble says,
B♭ A♭/B♭ B♭7

35
Do to oth - ers as you would have them do to you!
E♭ E♭/G B♭ A♭/C B♭/D
37
Do to oth - ers as you would have them do to you!
E♭ Cm7 B♭ F7 B♭
39
Do to oth- ers, do to oth- ers, do to oth- ers, yes you should,
B♭ A♭/B♭ B♭13 B♭ B♭ A♭/B♭ B♭13 B♭/A♭
41
do to oth- ers as you_ would have_ them_ do to you!
E♭/G C7sus E°7 Fm7 E♭/B♭ B♭ E♭ A♭ E♭

The Lord's Prayer

Our Father in heaven, hallowed be your name, your kingdom come, your will be done on earth as it is in heaven. Give us today our daily bread. Forgive us our debts, as we also have forgiven our debtors. And lead us not into temptation, but deliver us from the evil one.

Matthew 6:9-13

16
debts as we al - so have for - giv - en our debt - ors. And lead us
Asus A D/F♯ G D/F♯ Em7 D/A A13 A7 D
20
not in - to temp - ta - tion, but de - liv - er us from the e - vil
Em7 A/G D/F♯ Em7 D/A A7
24
one. Our
D Dsus Dsus D Bm7
1.
2.
27
Scripture may be spoken here
28
Em7 F♯m7 E/G♯ A G D/F♯

32
F♯/A♯ Bm Em7 A7sus A A/G D/F♯ G
36
Em7 A7sus A/G D/F♯ G Asus A D/F♯ G D/F♯ Em7
40
43
Our Fath - er in
D/A A13 A7 D Dsus D Bm7
44
heav - en, hal - low - ed be Your name. Your king - dom come, Your
Em7 F♯m7 E/G♯ A G D/F♯

48
will be done on earth as it is in heav'n. Give us to-day our
F♯/A♯ Bm Em7 A7sus A A/G D/F♯ G
52
dail-y bread. For-give us our debts as we al-so have for-
Em7 A7sus A/G D/F♯ G Asus A D/F♯ G D/F♯ Em7
56
giv-en our debt-ors. And lead us not in-to temp-ta-tion, but de-
D/A A13 A7 D Em7 A/G D/F♯
60
liv-er us from the e-vil one.
Em7 D/A A7 D Dsus D

This Is Love/Love the Lord Your God

This is love, not that we loved God, but that he loved us and sent
His Son- as an atoning sacrifice for our sins.
I John 4:10

Love the Lord your God with all your heart and with all your soul
and with all your strength.
Deuteronomy 6:5

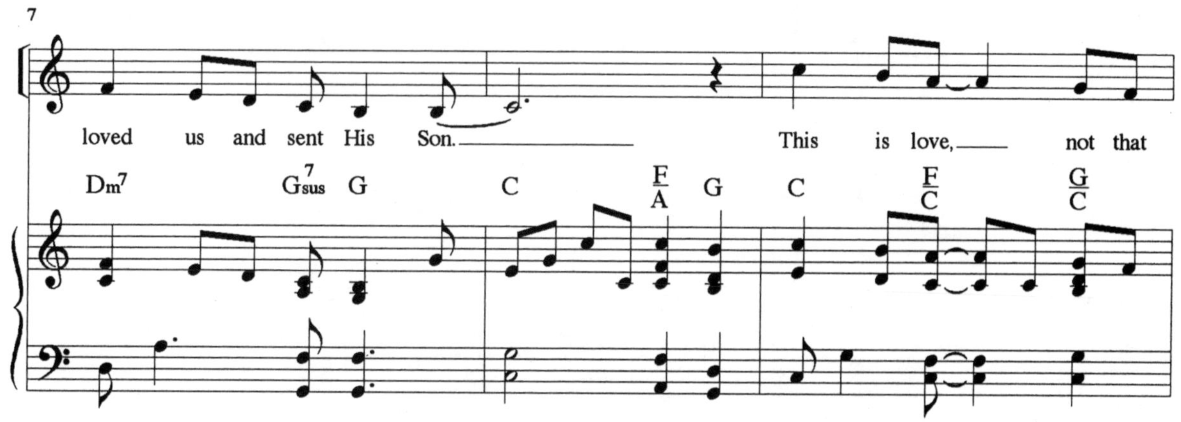

10
we loved God, but that He loved us and sent His Son as an a -
C Dm7 C/E Am7 Dm7 G7sus G C
13
ton - ing sac - ri - fice for our sins.
Dm7 G7sus Am Dm7 G C F
16
17
For Je - sus is the Son of God.
C F G/F F C/E Dm7 C
19
Je - sus is God's own Son. The Sav - ior of the
F G/F F C Csus C F G/F F

22
1.
world, our Re - deem - er and Friend! For
C/E Dm7 C Am7 Dm7 G13 G7 C Csus C
25
2.
26
Friend!
C C F/C G/C C Dm7 C/E Am7
28 Dm7 G7sus G C F/A G C F/C G/C
31 C Dm7 C/E Am7 Dm7 G7sus G C F/A G

34
This is love, not that we loved God, but that He loved us and sent His Son.
C F/C G/C C Dm7 C/E Am7 Dm7 G7sus G
37
This is love, not that we loved God, but that He
C F/A G C F/C G/C C Dm7 C/E Am7
40
loved us and sent His Son as an a - ton - ing sac - ri - fice
Dm7 G7sus G C Dm7 G7sus Am
43
for our sins. For
Dm7 G C F C

46
Je - sus is the Son of God.
Je - sus is God's own
F G/F F C/E Dm7 C F G/F F
49
Son. The Sav - ior of the world, our Re -
C Csus C F G/F F C/E Dm7 C Am7
52
54
deem - er and Friend!
Dm7 G13 G7 Csus C C F/C G/C
55
C Dm7 C/E Am7 Dm7 G7sus G C
Scripture may be spoken here

58
Csus
C
Csus

61
Love the Lord, your God.
Love Him with all your
C
Dm7
C/E

64
heart, and with all your soul, and with all your
Am
Dm7
G7sus
G

67
strength!
69
Scripture may be spoken here
C
Csus
C

These commandments that I give you today are to be upon your hearts. Impress them on your children. Talk about them when you sit at home and when you walk along the road, when you lie down and when you get up. Tie them us symbols on your hands and bind them on your foreheads. Write them on the door frames of your houses and on your gates.

Deuteronomy 6:5-9

NOTES

NOTES

NOTES

NOTES

NOTES

NOTES

NOTES